Curious George Grows a Garden

Written by Jessica Wollman

Houghton Mifflin Harcourt
Boston   New York

It's spring!
The snow has melted.
George has a plan!
He will plant a garden.

Curious George has everything he needs to plant a garden.
He has seeds.
He has a shovel.
He has water.

George digs holes with his shovel.
He plants seeds in the dirt.

Next, George waters
the seeds.
Seeds need water so they
can grow into plants.

The sun shines down on George's garden.
Plants need sunlight to grow.

George visits his garden every day.
He waters the soil.
He waits for the seeds to sprout.

Look, George!
A stem!
There are many more stems!
Your plants are growing!

And growing . . . and growing!
George has a garden!